T3-BVM-899

DREAMLAND

365

Maths Activity Book

Compiled by
Lata Seth
Anuj Chawla

DREAMLAND PUBLICATIONS

J-128, Kirti Nagar, New Delhi -110 015, India
Tel : +91-11-2510 6050, 2543 5657
E-mail : dreamland@dreamlandpublications.com
Shop online at www.dreamlandpublications.com
Follow us on www.instagram.com/dreamland.publications

Write the numbers that come before and after.   Colour the even numbers on the hens.

Multiply and match the answers with their respective numbers.

2 X 6=

3 X 5=

7 X 2=

2 X 8=

2 X 9 =

Find a way through the problems whose answer is 10 to reach the dog.

5 + 5 =

2 + 8 = 10 10   3 + 7 = 10

6 + 4 = 10   2 + 8 = 10   9 + 1 = 10

6 + 4 =

5 + 5 = 10   9 + 1 = 10

8 + 9 = 17   7 + 7 = 14

6 + 4 = 10

5 + 5 = 10   7 + 3 = 10   8 + 2 = 10

5 + 5 = 10

Write the missing number.

5

10

15

How many books are there?

6 + 2 = 8

There are ___8___ books

Tick the correct answer.

15 - 7 = 8

(7) (8) (6)

25 - 9 =

(14) (15) (16)

3

Write the numbers in order from the smallest to the greatest.

| 23 | 4 | 98 | 56 |

| 4 | 23 | 56 | 98 |

Fill in the missing numbers in the boxes below.

| 5 | 10 | 15 | 20 | 25 | 30 |

| 6 | 12 | 18 | 24 | 30 | 36 |

Let's start skip counting by 2.

Let's start skip counting by 3.

Let's start skip counting by 4.

2	3	4
4	6	8
6	9	12
8	12	16
10	15	20
12	18	24
14	21	28
16	24	32
18	27	36
20	30	40

Find the answers and colour according to the codes.

15 = Yellow   20 = Red

10 + 5 =

6 + 9 =

17 - 2 =

19 - 4 =

15 + 5 =

12 + 3 =

16 - 1 =

20 - 5 =

3 × 5 =

13 + 2 =

Take away 5 and write the correct answer.

$$10-5 = \enspace \textcircled{5}$$

Circle the set in each row that matches with the numbers shown.

12	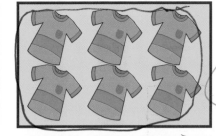	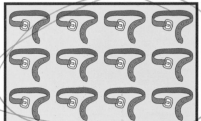
6	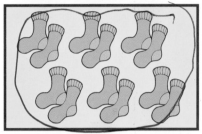	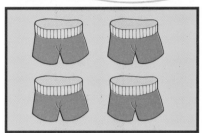
1	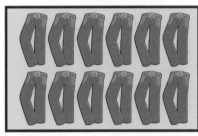	
4		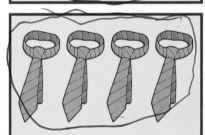

Solve the sums in the grid by filling in the missing numbers.

```
        14
        +
12  -   4   =   8
        =
2   +  18   =  20
```

Complete the order of the numbers on the caterpillar.

5 10 15 20 25 30 35 40

Solve the mirror sums.

$19 + 2 =$ ☐ $12 + 9 =$ ☐

$15 + 5 =$ ☐ $17 + 2 =$ ☐

Fill up the correct numbers in the blank squares.

6	+		=	14
+		+		+
	+		=	
=		=		=
13	+		=	23

Calculate the sums using the clues.
Write the answers in the blank boxes.

=7   =9   =8

− = ☐

× = ☐

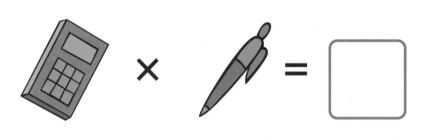

+ = ☐

◯

Count and encircle the correct number.

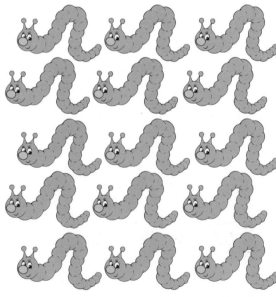

14	15	11	12

6

Find the answers of the multiplication problems.

$$\begin{array}{r} 9 \\ \times\ 7 \\ \hline \end{array}$$ $$\begin{array}{r} 8 \\ \times\ 6 \\ \hline \end{array}$$ $$\begin{array}{r} 7 \\ \times\ 5 \\ \hline \end{array}$$ $$\begin{array}{r} 6 \\ \times\ 4 \\ \hline \end{array}$$ $$\begin{array}{r} 6 \\ \times\ 8 \\ \hline \end{array}$$

Colour the elephant whose answer is biggest.

4 + 1 =

2 + 8 =

4 + 5 =

2 + 1 =

Find the answers and colour the picture.

10   15   20   25   30

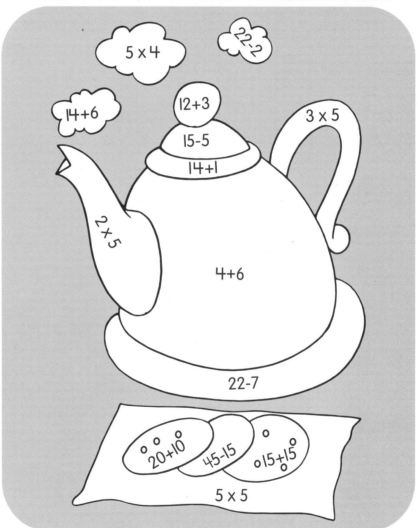

Which number comes next?

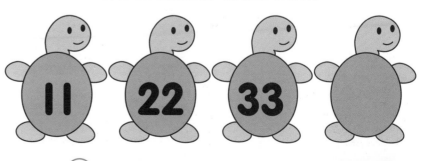

11   22   33

How many fish are there?

There are _____ fish.

Follow the codes and colour the pictures accordingly.

4 = ●   6 = ●   5 = ○   3 = ●   2 = ●   7 = ●

| 7-2 | 30-24 | 10-4 | 50-48 | 50-43 | 4-1 |

Which number comes next?

| 4 | 8 | 12 | 16 | 20 | 24 | |

Match the correct answers.

| 45 | 15 | 50 | 25 | 22 |

| 25+25 | 5 X 5 | 15+7 | 35+10 | 18-3 |

The numbers are placed in the triangle below so that each of the three sides total 12. Rearrange the numbers so that each side totals 9.

Count and tick the correct answer.

15

12

14

Match pairs of numbers that come together.

50   35   21   15   41   64

65   16   51   42   36   22

Count the objects and write the answers.

Colour the car with the number 12.

📚 = ◯   ✏️ = ◯   📄 = ◯

Write after and before numbers.

49

57

Follow the table of 5 and join the stars.

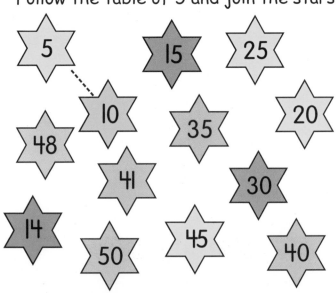

5   15   25

10   35   20

48   41   30

14   45   40

50

Follow the table of 3 to complete the rhino and colour it.

66
63
60
57
54
51
48
45
42
39
36
33
30
27
24
21
18
15
12
9
6
3

Encircle the problems whose answer is 30.

25 + 25 =

30

19 × 5 =

15 × 2 =

16 × 3 =

Solve the sums.

4 + 8 = ◯
9 + 3 = ◯

Colour the boxes with the bigger number.

9   5

12   15

21   27

Write the missing numbers.

1		3		5			8		10

11				15		17		19	

21		23			26			29	

31		33		35			38		40

	42		44			47		49	

Circle the correct number of frogs. Colour the frogs.

Add 6 to the numbers on each apple, and drop the apple whose number matches the number on the basket.

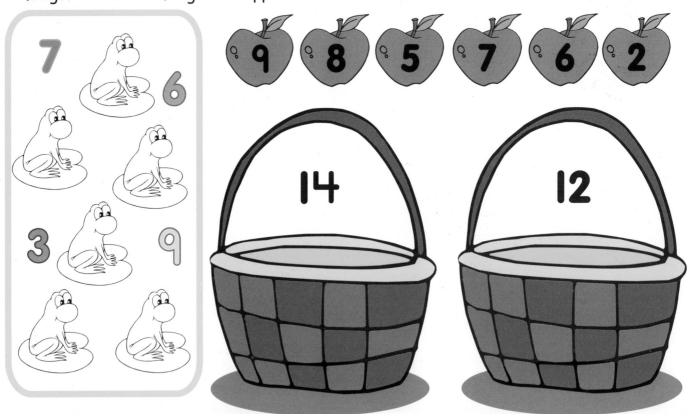

Which number comes next?

100	200	300	400	

100	99	98	97	

11	22	33	44	

100	105	110	115	

151	152	153	154	

Solve the math puzzle.

16	+	8	=	
+		-		+
4	-	4	=	
=		=		=
	+		=	24

Solve and write.

$1 \times 2 =$ $=$ ☐

$2 \times 2 =$ 2 $+$ 2 $=$ ☐

$3 \times 2 =$ 2 $+$ 2 $+$ 2 $=$ ☐

$4 \times 2 =$ 2 $+$ 2 $+$ 2 $+$ 2 $=$ ☐

$5 \times 2 =$ 2 $+$ 2 $+$ 2 $+$ 2 $+$ 2 $=$ ☐

Colour the given number of objects.

4

Write the missing numbers.

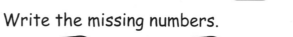

61		63		65

	67			70

Complete the pattern of reverse counting.

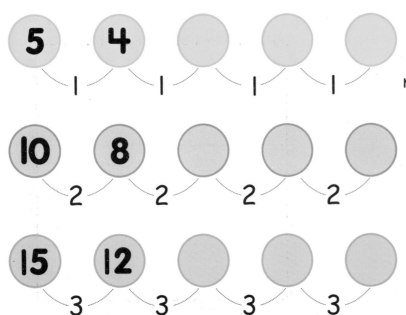

| 5 | 4 | | | |

1 — 1 — 1 — 1

| 10 | 8 | | | |

2 — 2 — 2 — 2

| 15 | 12 | | | |

3 — 3 — 3 — 3

Solve the sums in the grid by filling in the missing numbers.

```
            9
            +
  35  -         =
            =
      +  18  =  43
```

Find the product.

7
× 5
___

6
× 3
___

5
× 8
___

15
× 3
___

Look at the picture carefully and find the number of objects, as shown.

= ◯

= ◯

Draw a line to make a number pattern by counting in 2's.

Follow the colour code and colour.

1	2	3	4

Write the tens of each of the numbers.

47 = _____ tens

75 = _____ tens

93 = _____ tens

69 = _____ tens

Colour the pictures that have even numbers.

29

Draw a circle around the odd numbers.

How many times does the number 3 appear on the board? Write in the circle.

Let's enhance our maths skills by solving these problems.

a. $7 \times 2 =$

b. $5 \times 3 =$

c. $7 + 3 =$

a. [ ]

b. [ ]

c. [ ]

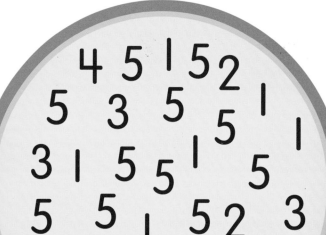

In each set, count and write the total number of pictures . Also write the half of it.

___altogether. Half is ___.

___altogether. Half is ___.

___altogether. Half is ___.

Join the dots and numbers.

What comes next? Write the missing numbers.

Fill the boxes with the correct numbers.

Colour the odd number balloons red and even number balloons yellow.

Tens	Ones

= _____

31

There is a pattern to this row of numbers.
Can you write in the missing numbers?

9, 18, _____, 36, 45, _____, 63

7, 14, _____, 28, 35, _____, 49

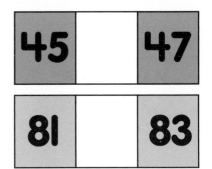

45		47
81		83

Draw the hands on the clock according to the time given.

12:00   7:30   5:15   2:45

Find the total and match them with the numbers on the petals.

68   47   32 +15

97   76   32 + 65

44   52   27 + 25

88   14   40 +48

32

Solve and write the answer.

15 × 3 _____

44 ÷ 4 _____

18 − 3 _____

17 + 40 _____

14 × 8 _____   10 × 7 _____

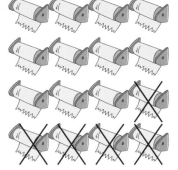

16 − 5 = ☐

Write the missing numbers.

10	12	___		16
___	20		___	24

Can you fill the missing numbers?

8	+		=	12
+		+		+
	+	8	=	
=		=		=
11	+		=	

Subtract and colour the fish.
20 = Yellow
10 = Red

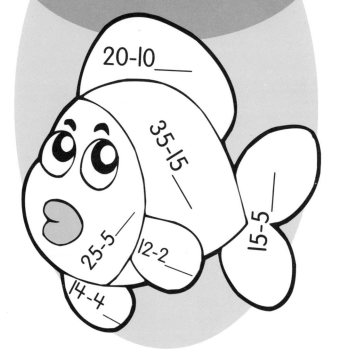

20−10 _____

35−15 _____

25−5 _____   12−2 _____   15−5 _____

14−4 _____

33

Solve the sums.

$$82 - 13 + 15 = \bigcirc$$

Take a route through the questions whose answers are 10 to help the man reach the snake.

5+5	90-80		13-3	25-15	
15-5	18+8	7+3		18-9	10-0
			18-8		9+1
7+3	75-65				14-4
	5x2		35-25		19-9
				27-17	8+5
12-2	2X5	11-1		1+5	
			9+1		10-2
5+5	6+4		17-7	3+7	12+8

Colour each number with a different colour.

1 3 2
7 4 5
6
10 8 9

Colour the hidden numbers from 1-6

Take each girl to her respective number. Hint: Look at the number name on the frock and match it with the number on the ball.

Complete the sums using the codes.

Colour the circles with the smallest number.

Put the pictures in the correct order.

Calculate the answers then match them with the numbers on the board.

$4 + 4 =$ ◯

$3 \times 3 =$ ◯

$9 \div 3 =$ ◯

$4 + 3 =$ ◯

$5 \times 2 =$ ◯

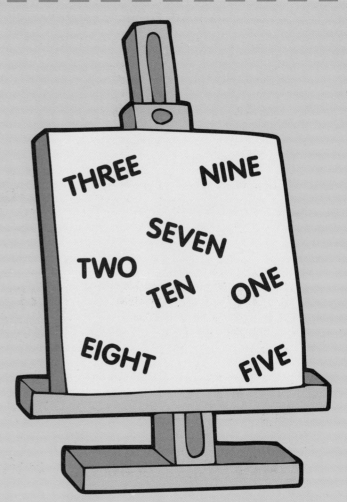

THREE NINE
SEVEN
TWO TEN ONE
EIGHT FIVE

Find the answers of the mathematical problems.

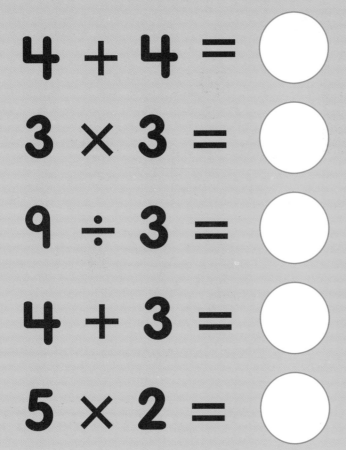

$$56 + 45$$

$$86 - 25$$

Count the starfish and write the answer in the circle.

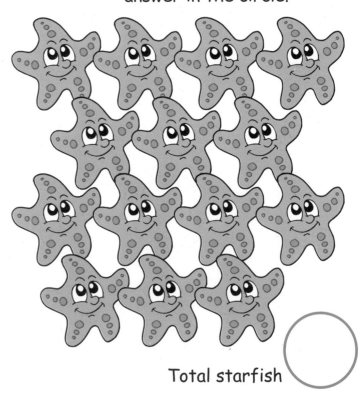

Total starfish ◯

Colour as many bananas as the given number.

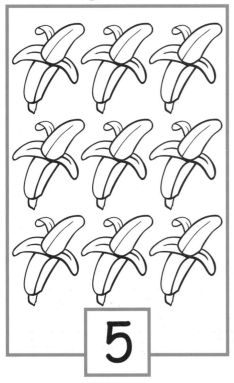

5

Join the numbers and complete the picture.

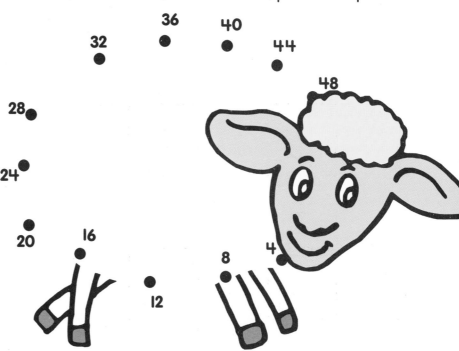

Match the numbers in the pictures with the numbers given in the circles.

1
2
3
4
5
6
7
8
9
10

Count the number of objects and tick the correct circle.

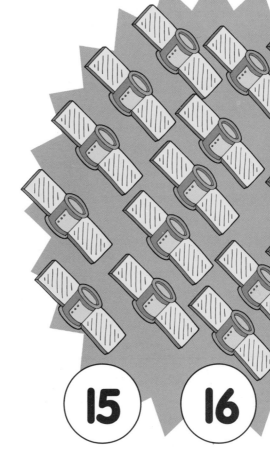

15 16 17

Fill the blank squares with the correct numbers.

7	+		=	12
+		+		+
	+	4	=	
=		=		=
8	+		=	

Match the answers to the problems with the correct digit.

4	3	1
9	7	2
5	0	6

12- 5   17- 10   13- 8

10 -1   20 -19   13- 6

Place the correct numbers in the circles and squares.

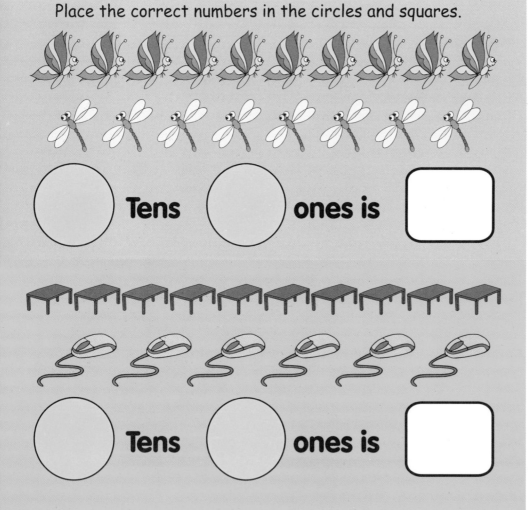

◯ Tens   ◯ ones is   ☐

◯ Tens   ◯ ones is   ☐

How many lotus flowers are there?

8+4 = ☐

3+1 = ☐

7+5 = ☐

2+3 = ☐

38

Write '-' and '=' between the numbers to show subtraction facts, and then, encircle the facts. The facts can be found by moving across or down. Two have been done for you.

15	5	6	10	4	9	8	1
4 – 3 = 1			7	2	1	6	5
12	4	8	3	2	7	4	9
2	4	1	15	8	– 3	6	2
7	6	14	5	9	= 4	8	0
4	14	5	9	6	3	2	16
3	7	9	3	6	9	6	8
12	7	5	10	6	4	1	8

Draw lines to join questions with answers.

9   18   23

15+8   9 X 2   14-5

Add up the objects.

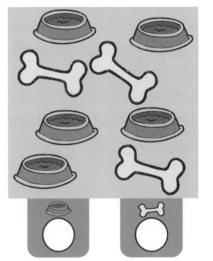

Jump and add the numbers to find the answers.

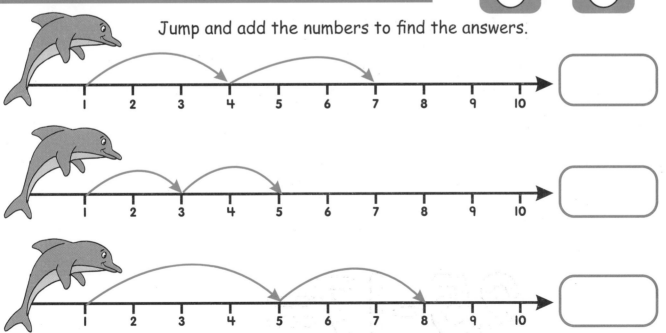

Write the missing numbers match them with the numbers in the boxes.

| 36 | 25 | 17 | 5 |

☐ + 15 = 20

20 + ☐ = 45

14 + ☐ = 50

30 + ☐ = 47

Count the objects and match them with their respective numbers.

5

4

12

9

Solve the subtraction problem. Colour the sofas to match the answer.

25-17= ◯

Match the pictures with the answers.

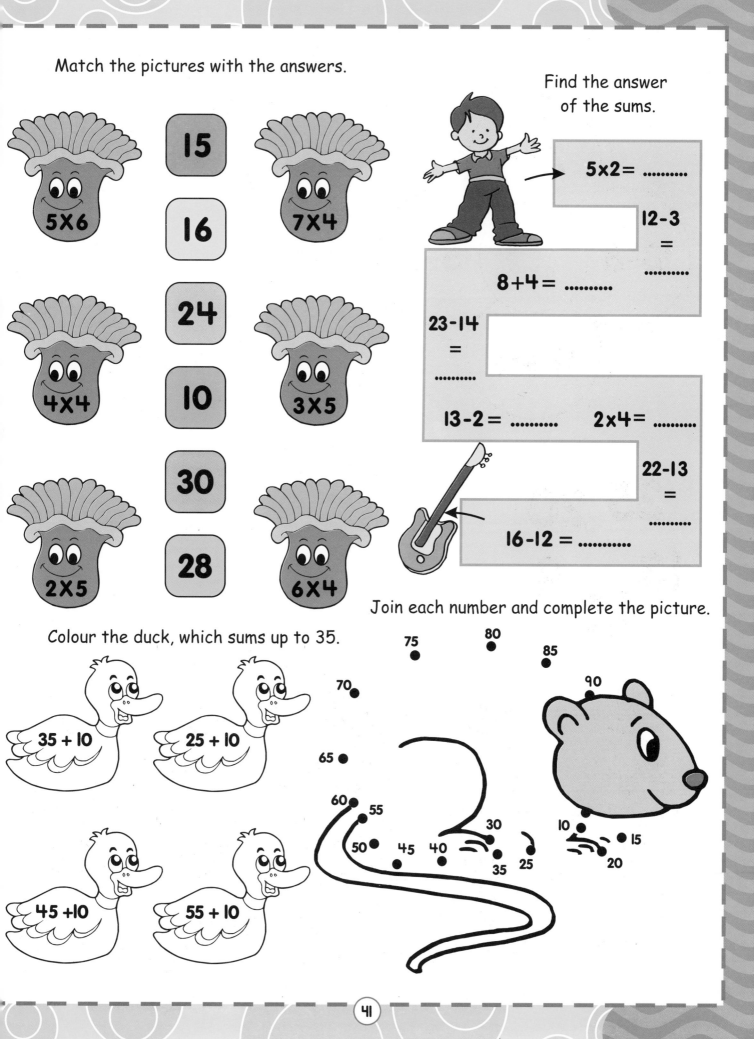

Find the answer
of the sums.

5×6

15

16

7×4

24

4×4

10

3×5

30

28

2×5

6×4

5x2= ....

12-3 =
    ....

8+4 = ...

23-14 =
    ....

13-2 = ...   2x4= ....

22-13 =
    ....

16-12 = ...

Join each number and complete the picture.

Colour the duck, which sums up to 35.

35 + 10

25 + 10

45 +10

55 + 10

41

Tick the digits or problems
whose answer is 10 or 25.

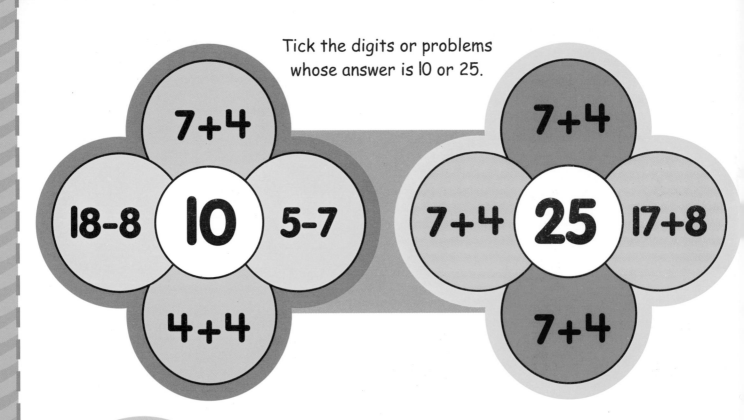

Write the numbers from the greatest to the smallest.

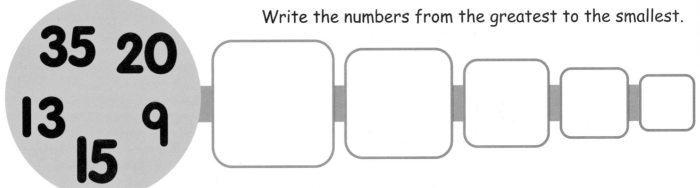

Complete the sequence of numbers.

Count the candles without the cross and write the answer.

5 × 5 = ☐

2 × 5 = ☐

4 × 4 = ☐

7 × 8 = ☐

7 × 2 = ☐

24 - 8 =

Solve the sums and write the answers.

⓪ ① ② ③ ④ ⑤ ⑥ ⑦ ⑧ ⑨ ⑩ ⑪ ⑫ ⑬ ⑭ ⑮ ⑯ ⑰ ⑱ ⑲ ⑳

12+7 = ☐

11+4 = ☐

8+8 = ☐

7+7 = ☐

5+6 = ☐

18+2 = ☐

43

Sum up the beautiful butterflies.

 +  = [ ]

[ ]   [ ]   [ ]

Write the correct numbers.

12	+		=	18
+		+		+
20	+		=	
=		=		=
	+	18	=	50

Add up the number of tomatoes

[ ]

Count and write how many pictures are there in each box?

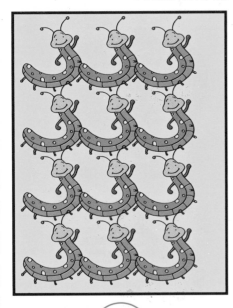      

( )   ( )   ( )

Read the clues on the sheep and write the numbers.

4 tens 4 ones   6 tens 3 ones   9 tens 1 ones

Colour the boxes that add up-to 9 to find the path from the dog to the food.

6+3	8+4	3+6	8+8	7+8
5+4	4+4	3+2	8+7	3+7
3+6	8+1	3+6	3+1	5+5
4+5	7+2	1+8	5+4	3+6

Colour the given
number of humming birds.

6

There are 8 balls, 2 more
balls are added to the group.
Draw and complete the sum.

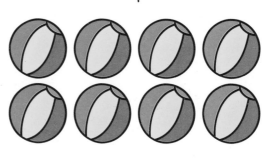

8 + __ = ☐

45

Look at the given sums. Help Jimmy to find the numbers so that each sum adds to the number 20.

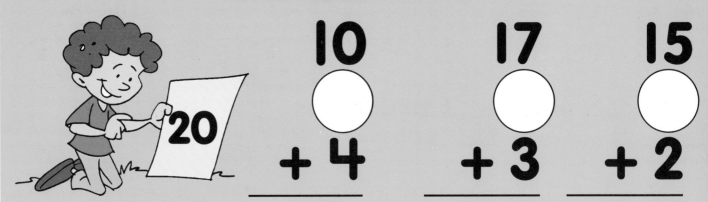

20

10
◯
+ 4
‾‾‾‾‾

17
◯
+ 3
‾‾‾‾‾

15
◯
+ 2
‾‾‾‾‾

Join the dots to complete and colour the picture.

Help Tommy to solve the sums.

10
6 in 2 out
5

Count the number of objects in each set and write the answer in the circle given below.

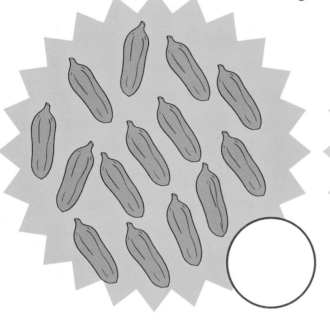

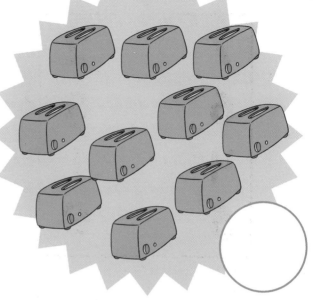

Solve the sums and match them with their correct solutions.

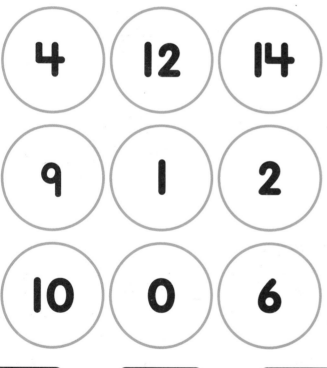

Count and encircle the total number of objects.

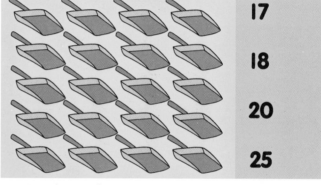

17

18

20

25

Look at the numbers written on the wings of the butterfly and write it in the blank space and solve the sum.

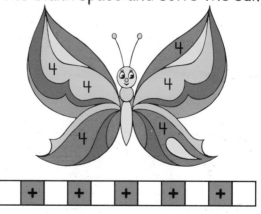

| | + | | + | | + | | + | | + | |

6 Times 4 = ☐

Draw a line to match the numbers which add up-to the number given in circles.

Count the total number of objects and write it in the given space.

Complete the sequence.

48

Look at the table, each number has a value. Using the value solve the fun puzzle.

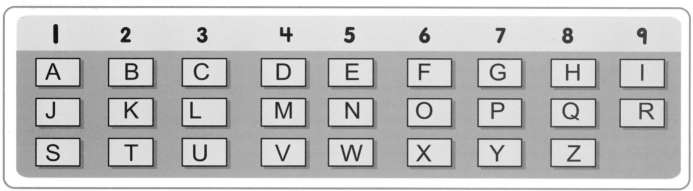

1	2	3	4	5	6	7	8	9
A	B	C	D	E	F	G	H	I
J	K	L	M	N	O	P	Q	R
S	T	U	V	W	X	Y	Z	

Calculate and find the worth of the name Spider Man ?

___ + ___ + ___ + ___ + ___ + ___ + ___ + ___ + ___
S   P   I   D   E   R   M   A   N

Total = ⬭

Use the picture code to solve the sums given below.

🍇	🥬	🍌	🍎	🍊
5	7	4	8	3

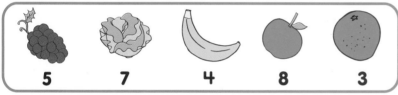

🥬 + 🍇 = ☐

🍌 + 🍎 = ☐

🍊 + 🥬 = ☐

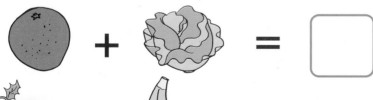

🍇 + 🍌 = ☐

Look at the numbers given on the teapot. Using the instructions match the teapots with the right cup.

1 more

Teapot	Cup
59	100
33	88
99	60
42	34
87	43

How many Tens and Ones are there in each row?

Tens	Ones

Tens	Ones

Tens	Ones

Help Johnny to match the sums with the correct answers.

Help Renie to complete the puzzle.

```
  35
  10
+  0
```

30

```
  16
  15
+  4
```

45

```
  10
  15
+  5
```

35

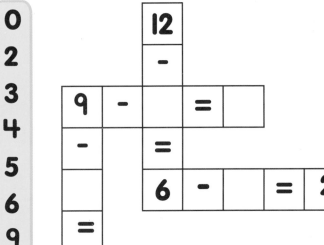

0
2
3
4
5
6
9

12				
-				

9	-		=	
-		=		
	6	-		=	2
=				
4	-	2	=	
		-		
11	-	2	=	
		=		

Match the numbers in each box so that their difference
is same as given inside the star.

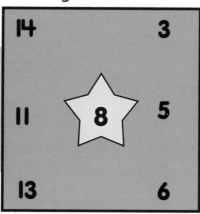

Solve and colour the boxes in red colour that show a sum of
16 and help the dog to reach his house.

Count the number
of pots and
write the correct
answer.

	15 +1	10 +6	18 +6
10 +10	10 +8	12 +4	21 +6
9 +4	8 +8	13 +3	13 +6
3 +1	12 +4	9 +5	14 +12
5 +6	14 +2	7 +9	

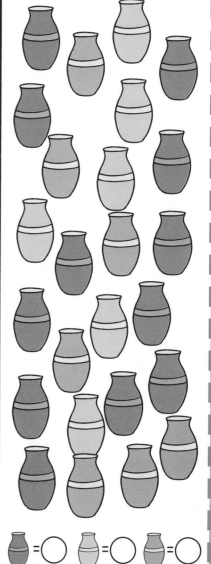

Join the stars with multiples of 7.

Write the numbers that comes before.

7   21   42
14   35
25   49
28
72   56
30
70   63

76   88

Use the instructions and match the rabbits with their correct numbers on the carrots.

Count the total number of mushrooms.

1 less

20
25
70
80
55

69
79
54
19
24

Total Mushrooms ☐

Colour the chicks with even numbers

Complete the puzzle.

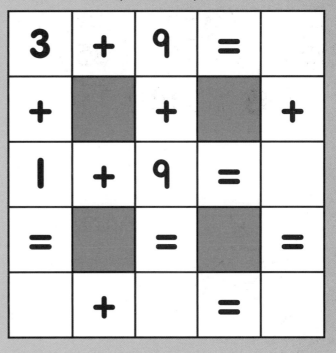

3	+	9	=	
+		+		+
1	+	9	=	
=		=		=
	+		=	

Use the number line to add the sums in each row.

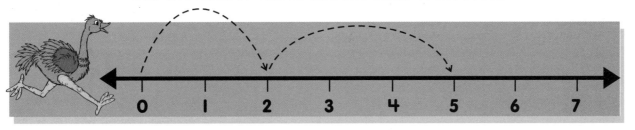

2 + 3 = ☐

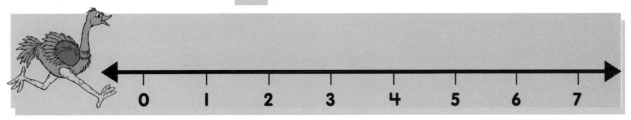

4 + 2 = ☐

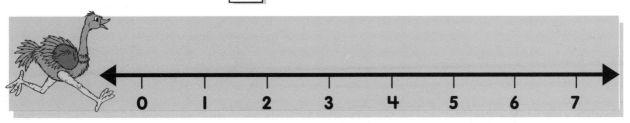

3 + 2 = ☐

Write the numbers in increasing order.

45 25 35 15 10

☐ ☐ ☐ ☐ ☐

Help Jacky to reach and eat the delicious ice cream by solving the sums.

6 + 3 = ___

7 + 5 = ___

4 + 3 = ___

2 + 5 = ___

8
+ 5
___

2 + 1 = ___

4 + 5 = ___

9
+ 3
___

7 + 7 = ___

6 + 7 = ___

2
+ 7
___

5 + 0 = ___

9 + 7 = ___

Write the numbers that comes after.

14 ☐
13 ☐
16 ☐
15 ☐
12 ☐
17 ☐

Help Tammy to match the numbers
on the fish which add up to 9.

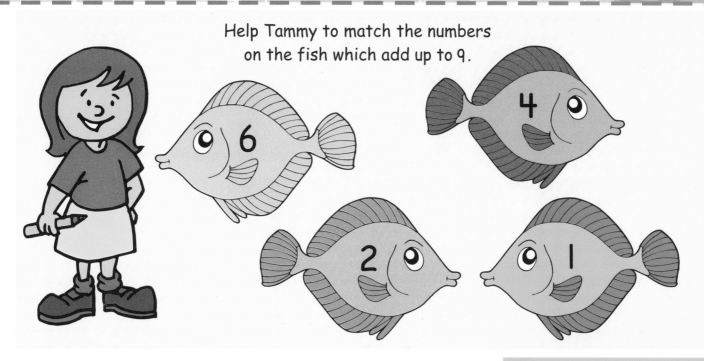

Colour the butterflies according to the given number.

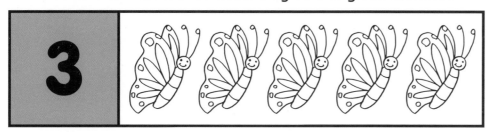

3

Look at the grid below. Join numbers to make 14 .
You can move across, down, left or right. You can
use a number more than once.

3	7	6	2	6	3	8
1	5	4	4	1	4	2
4	8	4	8	6	7	5
1	7	2	5	4	3	2
6	5	3	7	4	1	7
4	3	5	8	6	3	5

Write half of the given
numbers in each set.

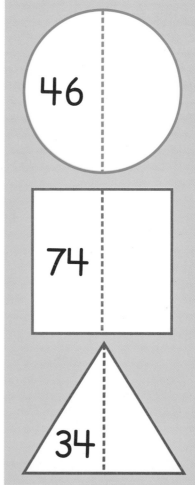

46

74

34

Cross out the number of objects in each row according to
the sums given and write the answer.

$15 - 5 =$ ☐

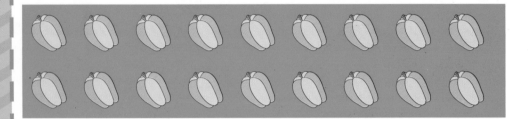

$18 - 7 =$ ☐

$20 - 6 =$ ☐

Solve the given sum.

Jack had____bananas.

Mom gave him____bananas.

Now Jack has____bananas.

Add the numbers.

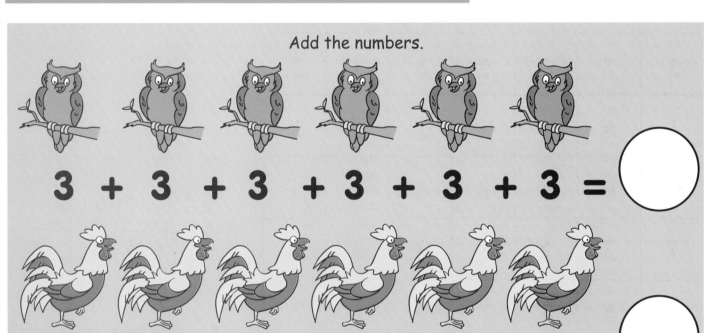

$3 + 3 + 3 + 3 + 3 + 3 =$ ◯

$4 + 4 + 4 + 4 + 4 + 4 =$ ◯

Count the objects in each column and write the answers.

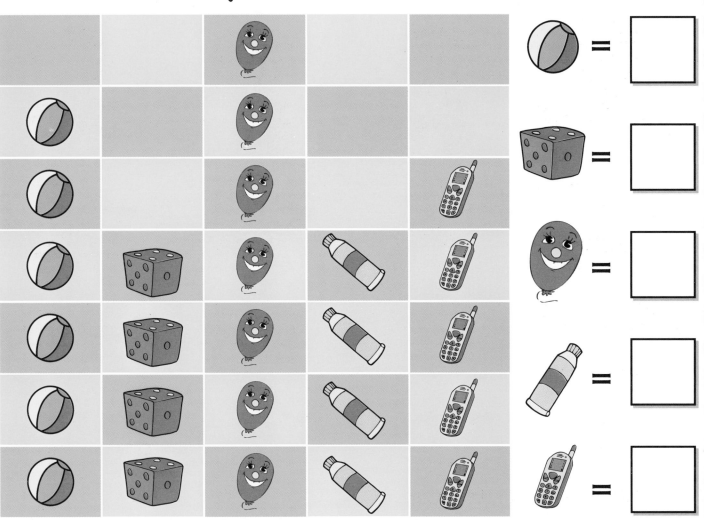

Match the sums to their correct answers.

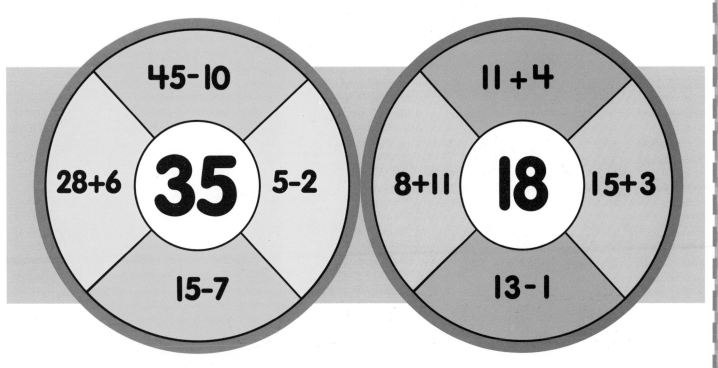

45-10

28+6   35   5-2

15-7

11+4

8+11   18   15+3

13-1

Read the number names and write half of the numbers as given in the example.

Eight
4

Twelve

Four

Ten

Fourteen

Two

Sixteen

Six

Tick the even and odd numbers.

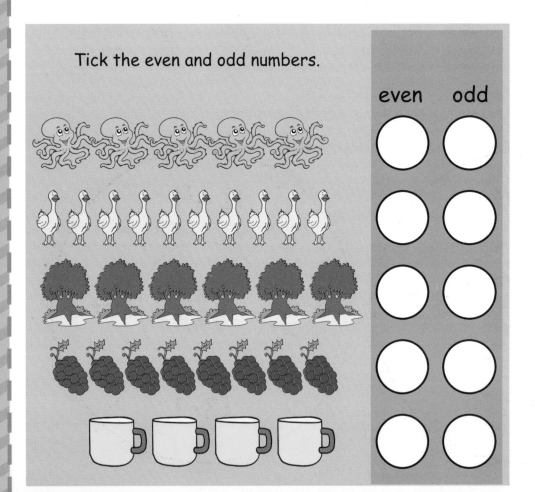

even   odd

Colour the cub whose multiple is 45.

3 X 5

5 X 9

5 X 5

Complete the following sums.

1. △△△ + △△ + △

   = [　　　　]

2. △△△ X △△△

   = [　　　　]

Complete the following patterns.

a) ⭐66　⭐67 → ⭐(　)

b) ⭐85　⭐86 → ⭐(　)

Solve the following sum.

$\begin{array}{r} 4 \\ -3 \\ +2 \\ \times 2 \\ \hline = \bigcirc \end{array}$

Use the picture code to do the following sums.

🐕 = 7　🐞 = 4　🐫 = 5　🐢 = 9　🐛 = 2　🦊 = 3

(a) 🐢 + 🐛 = _____

(b) 🐕 - 🐫 = _____

(c) 🦊 + 🐞 = _____

(d) 🐫 + 🐛 = _____

(e) 🐢 - 🐞 = _____

Help Jinny and Johnny to write the numbers that comes in between.

How many Tens are there?

87 = _____ tens

75 = _____ tens

23 = _____ tens

69 = _____ tens

Add the following numbers.

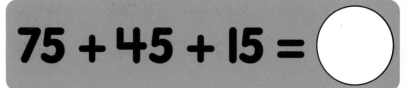

$$75 + 45 + 15 = \bigcirc$$

Solve the sums and use the number code to colour the picture.

Add 3 to each number given below and write answers in the blank circles.

+3

3
4
5
6

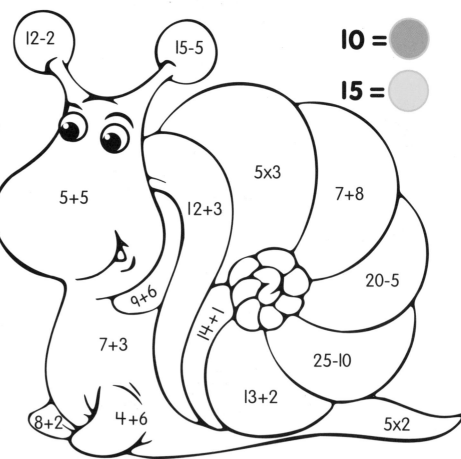

12-2

15-5

5+5

5x3

7+8

12+3

9+6

14+1

20-5

7+3

25-10

13+2

8+2

4+6

5x2

10 = ⬤

15 = ⬤

Solve the following sums and colour the boxes blue whose sum is 10 and red whose sum is 20.

10 +10	13 + 7	14 + 6	5 + 6	6 + 4
17 + 3	8 + 2	19 + 1	11 + 9	9 + 1
12 5 + 5	7 2 + 1	18 1 + 1	6 2 + 2	5 4 + 1
4 + 6	9 + 11	2 + 8	5 + 15	8 + 12
1 1 + 8	15 4 + 1	14 5 + 1	3 6 + 1	13 6 + 1

Write the multiples of 8.

80

64

[ ]

[ ]

16

[ ]

56

[ ]

24

8

Look at the numbers given in the first row and match them with the numbers that comes after in the second row.

15   47   85   41

42   86   16   48

Add and write the numbers so that the sum of each is 55.

55

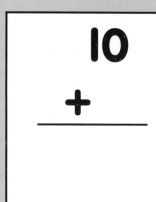

10
+ ___

25
+ ___

30
+ ___

Use the colour code to colour the pumpkin.

1   2   3   4

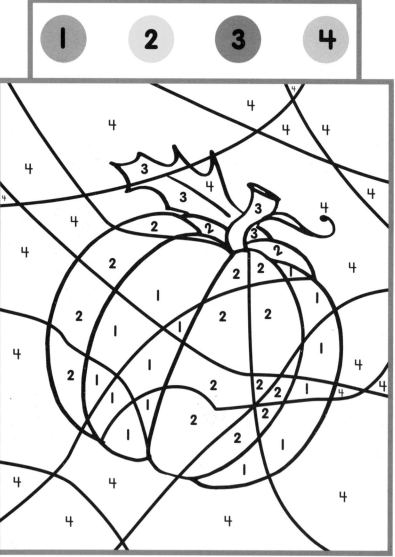

Look at the sea animals and write similar numbers on the sea animals given below.

25   75

95   66

62

Help the boys to solve the puzzle.

1 2 3 4 5 6 7 8 9 10

Count the given objects in each box and write the answer.

How many ovals are there?

How many  ? _____

Solve the following sums and write their answers in the correct place.

a. $3 \times 1 =$ d. $19 + 2 =$

b. $4 \times 2 =$ e. $12 - 5 =$

c. $5 + 4 =$ f. $18 \div 2 =$

a. [ ]   d. [ ]

b. [ ]   e. [ ]

c. [ ]   f. [ ]

Solve the sum.

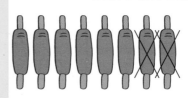   

Write the missing numbers.

51	52		54	
	57			60

Count and colour the vegetables given below.

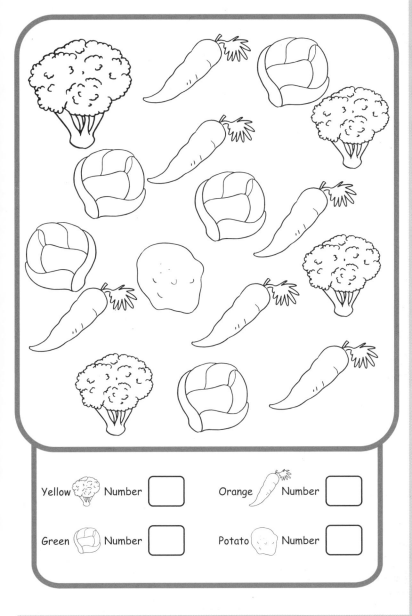

Yellow [image] Number ☐   Orange [image] Number ☐

Green [image] Number ☐   Potato [image] Number ☐

Write the number that has been frequently repeated in each bowl.

Match the frogs with the correct leaves.

Add and colour the boxes in red whose sum is **9**. Now join the red boxes and help Jacky to reach his pet Dog

5+3	8+1	3+6	8+8	7+8
5+4	4+5	3+2	8+7	3+7

3+6	8+1	6+3	3+1	5+5
4+5	7+2	2+7	9+0	5+4

Solve the multiplication sums.

Colour the capsicum green whose sum is 18.

5 × 2 =
=

6 × 2 =
=

7 × 2 =
=

8 × 2 =
=

9 × 2 =
=

12+8

2 × 9

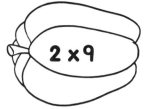

10+9

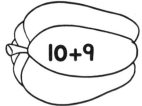

24-6

3 × 6

Solve the equation.

80

_ + _ = 80

_ + _ = 80

_ + _ = 80

Match the objects with the correct answers.

5

7

3

6

4

8

Write the correct time in each box.

☐ o' clock   ☐ o' clock   ☐ o' clock

Encircle the odd numbers.

52   45   35   10   11

14   19   16   25   59

Read the number names then write the correct numbers on each door.

70 — seventy   thirty   sixty   forty   fifty   twenty   ten

Match the vases with their correct flowers.

27   8×2   28   16

5×8   5×2   4×7

9×3   10   40   4×5   20

Count the fish and multiply it with number 7 to get the answer.

×

7

=

( )

Write the missing numbers to complete the table of ten.

10 times table

1	×	10	=	10
☐	×	10	=	20
3	×	☐	=	☐
☐	×	10	=	40
5	×	☐	=	☐
6	×	10	=	60
7	×	10	=	70
☐	×	☐	=	☐
9	×	10	=	90
10	×	☐	=	☐

Take help of the mirror to solve the sums.

☐ = 55 - 5

☐ = 86+ 9

Solve the addition sums given below.

15 + 2 = ____

18 + 9 = ____

Count the caterpillars and encircle the correct answer.

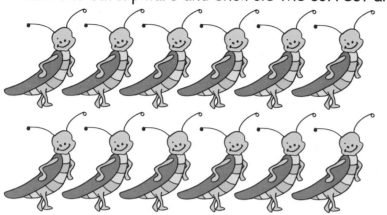

11
10
12

Using the instruction, colour the shapes in each column.

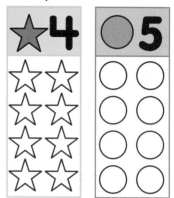

Add 6 to each number given below and help the butterfly reach the last flower.

Solve the following sums.

```
T O
1 5
+ 3 3
_____
```

```
T O
9 2
- 1 2
_____
```

```
T O
6 1
+ 2 7
_____
```

```
T O
7 9
- 2 5
_____
```

70

Join the dots to complete and colour the picture.

Look at the numbers and draw exact number of dice in the blank spaces. One is done for you.

⑥

⑤

④

Colour the boxes that give the answer as 8 to find the path from the teacher to the books.

2-1	5-3	7-2	8-1	9-3
8-4	15-7	20-12	9-1	16-8
10-2	12-4	14-6	5-2	7-5	11-3
7-5	8-6	6-1	9-5	

Solve the sums.

+ =

+ =

+ =

Encircle the odd numbers.

2 3 1 4 9

15 6 3 8 8

5 1 3 8 14

13 15 5 7 2

12 11 3

9 7 11 9 3

Write the correct sequence of the picture given below.

How many goats are there? Count and write the answer.

Fill in the missing blanks to get an answer written on the T.V.

Solve the fun puzzle.

	+	6	=	11
+		+		+
6	+		=	
=		=		=
	+	11	=	22

Complete the sequence.

2, 2, 3, 4, 5, 2, _, _, _, _, _

3, 2, 1, 4, 5, 3, _, _, _, _, _

3, 3, 7, 5, 4, 3, _, _, _, _, _

5, 5, 4, 3, 2, 5, _, _, _, _, _

Solve the sums given in each row.

 +5 = ◯

 +8 = ◯

 +9 = ◯

Solve the sums and use the colour code given below to colour the bear.

◯ = 12   ◯ = 15   ◯ = 16

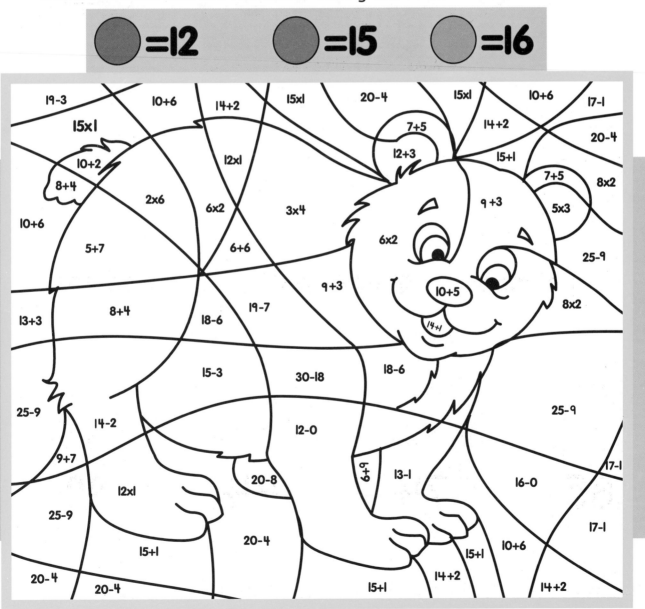

73

Solve the sums given below.

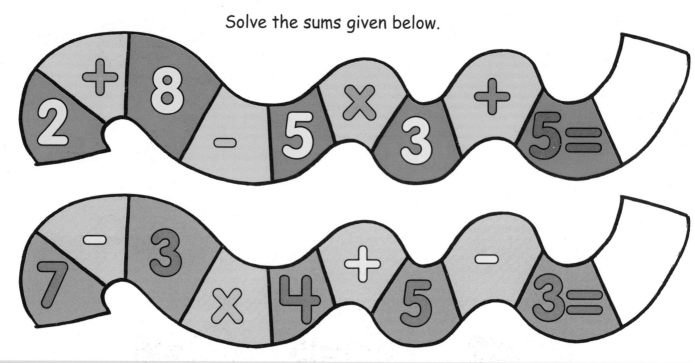

What is the time in each clock?

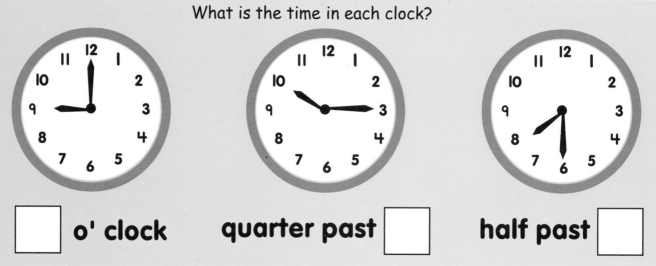

o' clock [ ]   quarter past [ ]   half past [ ]

How many tens are there in each placard?

85 [8]   74 [ ]   44 [ ]   99 [ ]

Multiply each number in the wheel with number 4 and write the answer in the blank circles.

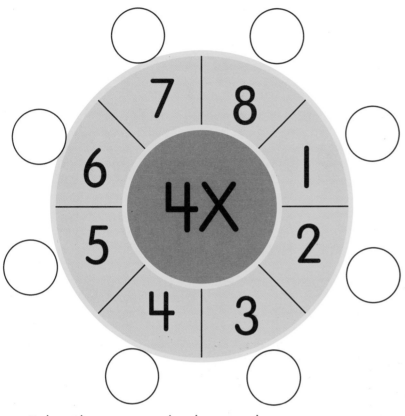

Count the objects in each row and encircle the right answer.

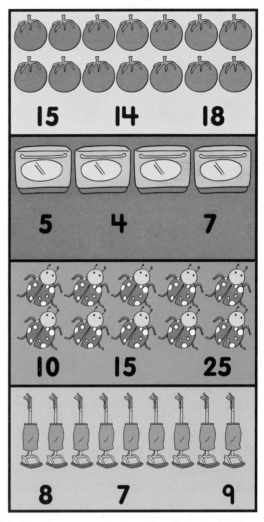

15	14	18
5	4	7
10	15	25
8	7	9

Solve the sums and colour each tortoise green whose answer is 50.

15-5   35+15   45-15

25x2   **50**   10x5

14+15   25+25   17+5

Help Jimmy to match the numbers with their correct number names.

Six   Eight

6

Four   9

4

8

Nine

Solve the following sums.

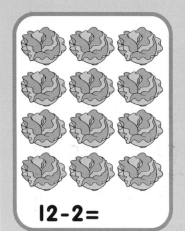

12-2=

20-5=

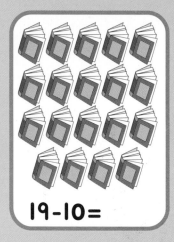

19-10=

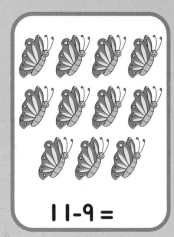

11-9 =

| 7 | 5 | 4 | 5 | 3 | 9 | 10 | 12 | 3 | 2 | 1 | 13 | 15 | 14 |

Help Joey and Philip to do the sum.

15+4=?

35+8=?

How many frogs are there?

 +

_____ frogs   _____ frogs   _____ frogs altogether.

Look at the sums and help Billy to solve them.

12×2 =

24 ◯
30 ◯
35 ◯
40 ◯

4×8 =

47 ◯
15 ◯
32 ◯
28 ◯

76

Help the dog to reach his house by solving the sums.

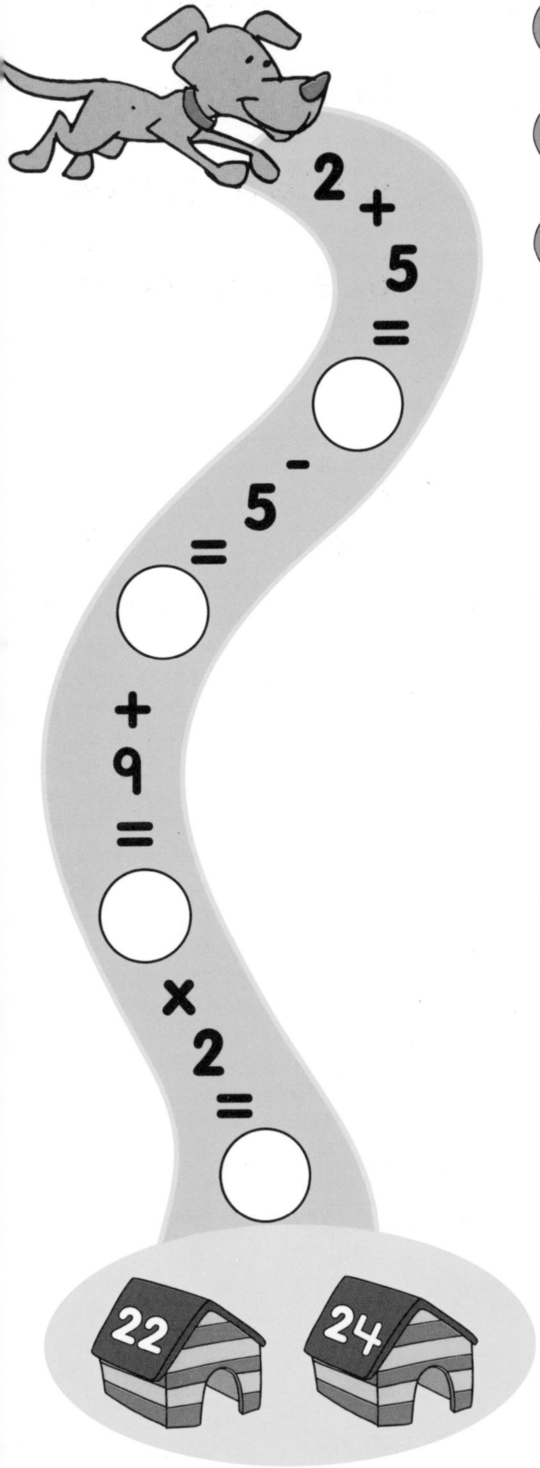

2 + 5 =
5 - =
+ 9 =
× 2 =

22   24

Write the missing number.

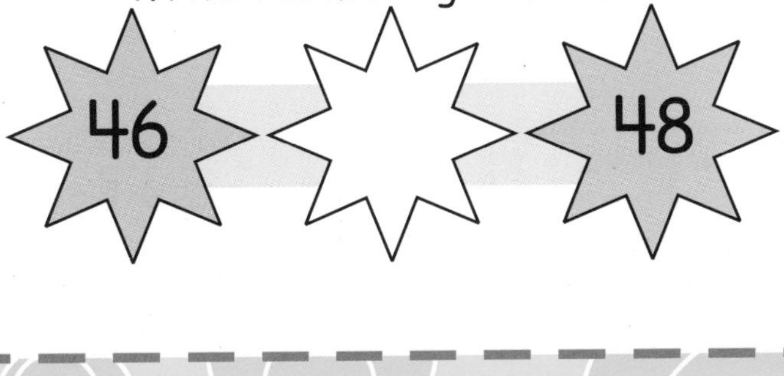

46   ☆   48

Solve the subtraction sums.

____ − ____ = ____

____ − ____ = ____

Count and write the number of type of dots on the tortoise, and then colour them.

Big Dots ● = _____   Small Dots ○ = _____

Solve the sums.

2 Balls	9 Balls	5 Balls	=	_____ Balls altogether.
5 Books	7 Books	2 Books	=	_____ Books altogether.
4 Pencils	8 Pencils	3 Pencils	=	_____ Pencils altogether.
6 Roses	9 Roses	4 Roses	=	_____ Roses altogether.

Match the division sums with their correct answers.

There are 10 ice-creams, if 2 are eaten. How many are left?

_____

Colour the dices in each set to get the given numbers.

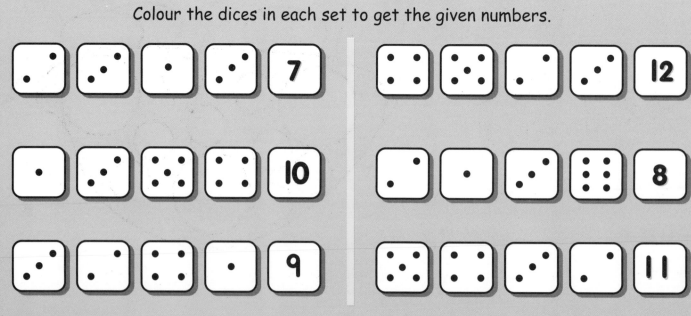

Look at the example and solve the sum.

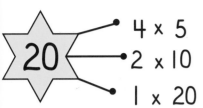

20 → 4 x 5
   → 2 x 10
   → 1 x 20

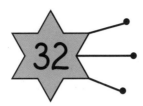

32

24

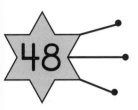

48

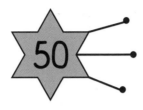

50

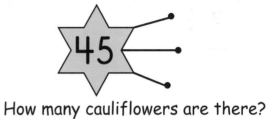

45

Count the total number of objects and write the answers.

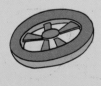 

How many cauliflowers are there?

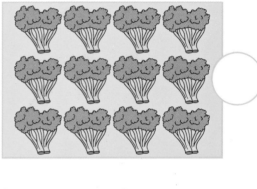

Fill the blanks with numbers so that the answer is 100 for all.

100

___ x ___

___ x ___

___ x ___

___ x ___

79

Match the circles with the correct rectangles.

| 1 + 2 | 1 | 4 + 1 | 2 | 4 + 2 | 4 |

| 3 | 1 + 1 | 5 | 3 + 1 | 6 | 1 + 0 |

Join the dots to complete and colour the picture.

Write the ">", "<" or "=" symbol.

| 6 ___ 9 | 10 ___ 10 |
| 11 ___ 8 | 16 ___ 19 |

Solve the sums.

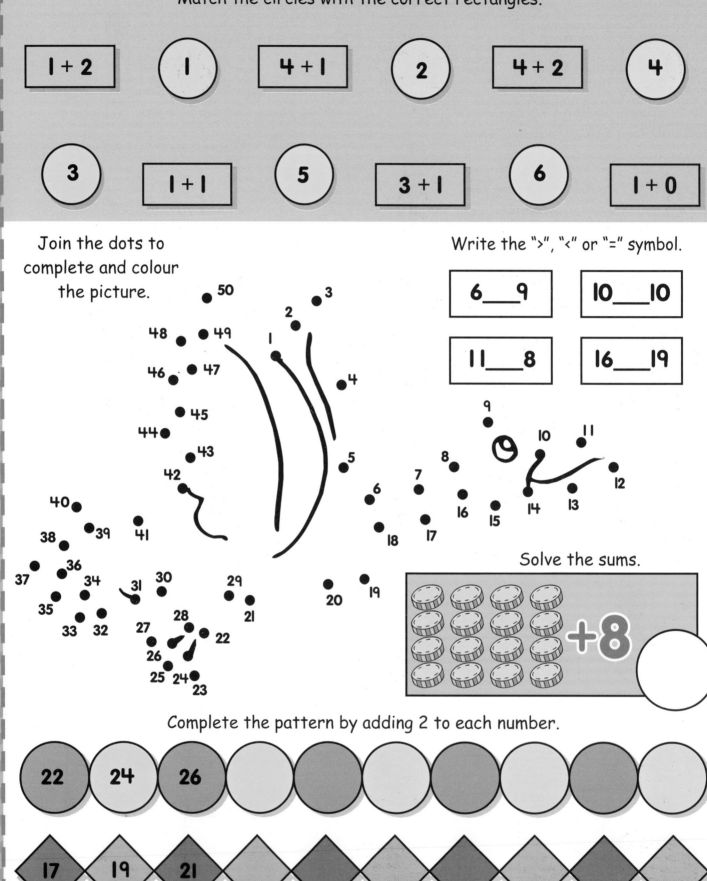

+8

Complete the pattern by adding 2 to each number.

| 22 | 24 | 26 | | | | | | | |

| 17 | 19 | 21 | | | | | | | |

80

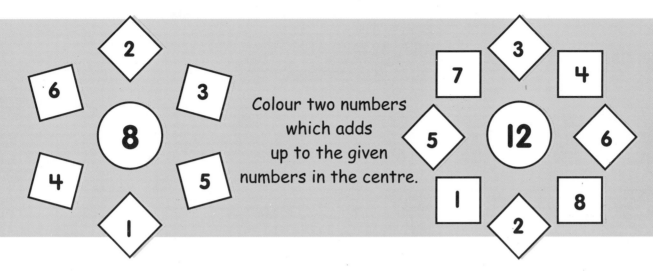

Colour two numbers which adds up to the given numbers in the centre.

Help the kids to find the answers.

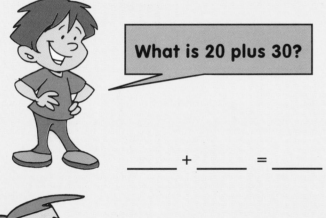

How much is 14 and 12?

_____ + _____ = _____

What is 20 plus 30?

_____ + _____ = _____

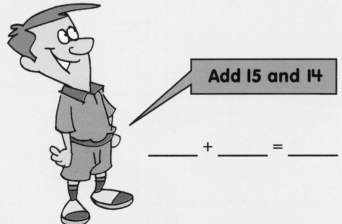

Add 15 and 14

_____ + _____ = _____

Complete the pyramid by filling in the blanks. One has been done for you. Hint: The number in the top square is the product of numbers in the two squares below it.

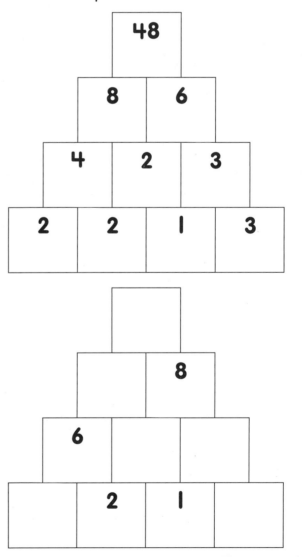

Match the multiplication sums with their correct answers.

8 × 6

32

7 × 9

48

63

6 × 6

36

16×2

Help Josey to reach the soup bowl by adding 1 to each number.

Look at each dice and write the correct numbers on them to get the multiple as 30.

31	32	41	32	34	38
24	33	62	83	35	23
68	34	35	18	38	39
26	67	36	37	40	50
93	25	19	21	41	51
14	89	43	42	52	27
56	15	45	44	53	18
75	46	47	48	49	50

×

=

30

Read the instructions and solve the sums.

Colour 3 marbles blue and I red. ⃝ ⃝ ⃝ ⃝ ___ + ___ = 4

Colour 2 marbles blue and 2 red. ⃝ ⃝ ⃝ ⃝ ___ + ___ = 4

Colour 4 marbles blue and none red. ⃝ ⃝ ⃝ ⃝ ___ + ___ = 4

Colour I marble blue and 3 red. ⃝ ⃝ ⃝ ⃝ ___ + ___ = 4

Divide:

$2 \div 2 =$ ___

$8 \div 2 =$ ___

$9 \div 3 =$ ___

$12 \div 3 =$ ___

$15 \div 3 =$ ___

$20 \div 2 =$ ___

Solve the division sums.

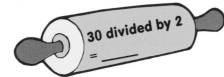
30 divided by 2 = ___

18 divided by 3 = ___

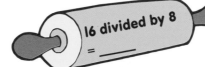
16 divided by 8 = ___

45 divided by 9 = ___

20 divided by 5 = ___

50 divided by 10 = ___

Solve the multiplication sums.

 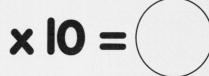 x 10 = ⃝

Solve the multiplication sums.

$3 \times$ ___ $= 0$

$3 \times$ ___ $= 12$

$3 \times$ ___ $= 18$

$3 \times 5 =$ ___

$3 \times 8 =$ ___

$3 \times$ ___ $= 30$

$3 \times$ ___ $= 33$

$3 \times$ ___ $= 21$

Help the kids to solve the division and multiplication sums.

_____ ÷ 3 = 7

3 x _____ = 21

18 ÷ 2 = _____

9 x _____ = 18

15 ÷ _____ = 3

5 x _____ = 15

24 ÷ 4 = _____

4 x _____ = 24

_____ ÷ 3 = 10

_____ x 10 = 30

Count the objects and circle the right answer.

21

22

23

24

Colour the boxes in each set to get the number 20.

| 2 | 5 | 12 | 3 |

| 6 | 7 | 4 | 10 |

| 7 | 4 | 3 | 9 |

| 2 | 14 | 4 | 5 |

Solve the sums in different ways to obtain the answer given in the centre.

Count the objects in the jar and write the answer.

Colour the boxes in red which help Jacky to get the answer 24.

| 12 + 12 | 10 + 7 | 2 + 14 | 18 + 6 |

8 + 9   3 + 14   8 + 8   4 + 9

19 + 5   6 + 11   20 + 2   4 + 13

6 + 9

24

2 + 15

Look at the numbers in each column and join them so that their answer is 15.

A

4

6

10

8

3

B

9

7

11

12

5

There are 5 burgers in the picture.
3 more burgers have been added to it. How many burgers are there in all?

5 + __ = [ ]

Colour two mangoes to get the answer 13.

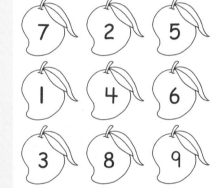

7   2   5

1   4   6

3   8   9

Tick the correct answer in each row.

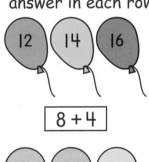

12   14   16

8 + 4

33   32   31

18 + 14

Colour two babies which add upto 10.

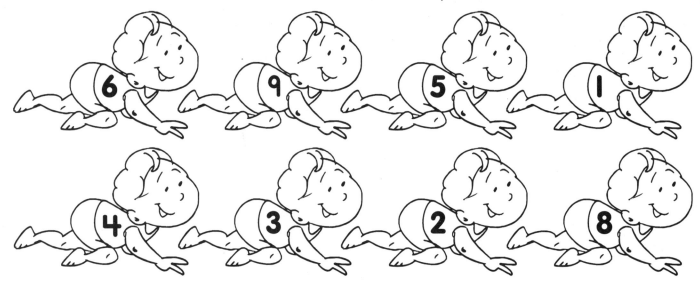

Write the missing numbers.

$$35 \quad \boxed{} \quad 37 \quad \boxed{} \quad 39$$

Count the horses and write the correct answer.

Help Tom to do the sums. Put a tick ✓ or a ✗ to each sum.

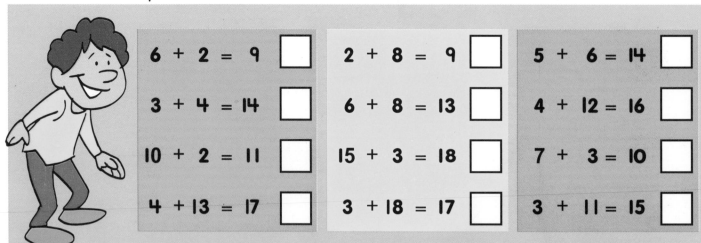

6 + 2 = 9 ☐	2 + 8 = 9 ☐	5 + 6 = 14 ☐
3 + 4 = 14 ☐	6 + 8 = 13 ☐	4 + 12 = 16 ☐
10 + 2 = 11 ☐	15 + 3 = 18 ☐	7 + 3 = 10 ☐
4 + 13 = 17 ☐	3 + 18 = 17 ☐	3 + 11 = 15 ☐

Complete the number sequence.

| 235 | 234 | 235 | 235 | 234 | _ _ _ |

Encircle the numbers that add upto 45.

30 + 5   3 + 18

35+ 10   25+20

3 + 14   **45**   7 + 13

43+2   4 +16

2 + 18   11 + 8

Draw hand on the digital clocks to show the time.

5 : 10

4 :20

5 :30

Solve the addition sums.

8	11	9	4	8
+5	+4	+8	+6	+3
___	___	___	___	___

Count the red and green cups on each table and find the sums.

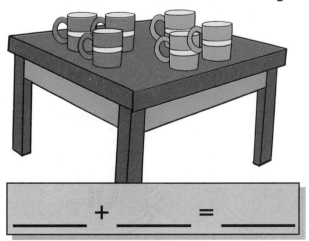

____ + ____ = ____

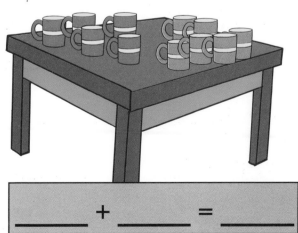

____ + ____ = ____

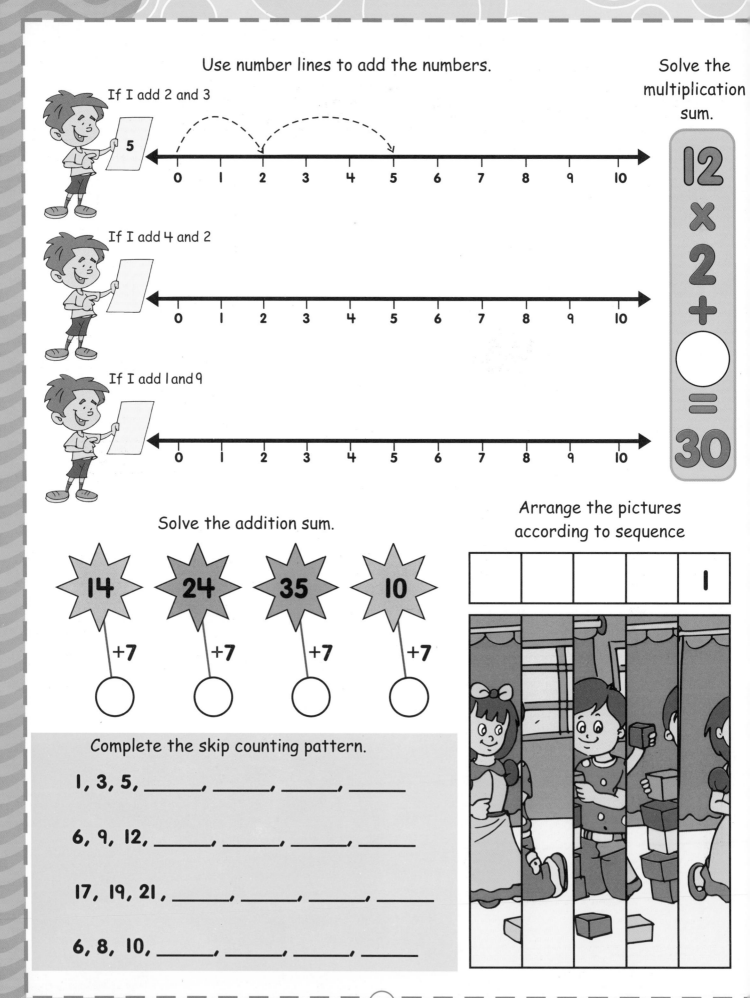

Use number lines to add the numbers.

Solve the multiplication sum.

If I add 2 and 3

5

0 1 2 3 4 5 6 7 8 9 10

If I add 4 and 2

0 1 2 3 4 5 6 7 8 9 10

If I add 1 and 9

0 1 2 3 4 5 6 7 8 9 10

12 × 2 + ○ = 30

Solve the addition sum.

14 +7 ○

24 +7 ○

35 +7 ○

10 +7 ○

Arrange the pictures according to sequence

				1

Complete the skip counting pattern.

1, 3, 5, _____, _____, _____, _____

6, 9, 12, _____, _____, _____, _____

17, 19, 21, _____, _____, _____, _____

6, 8, 10, _____, _____, _____, _____

Use the colour codes to colour the sunflowers.

4 Pink   5 Orange   6 Green   7 Yellow   8 Blue   9 Red

3+5   8-4   3×2

20÷4   2+5   17-8

Solve the sum in each set.

◯ + ◯ + ◯ = **88**

◯ + ◯ + ◯ + ◯ = **64**

Add the numbers.

9 + 8 = ◯

4 + 3 = ◯

8 + 1 = ◯

Colour the circles on each coin to get 10.

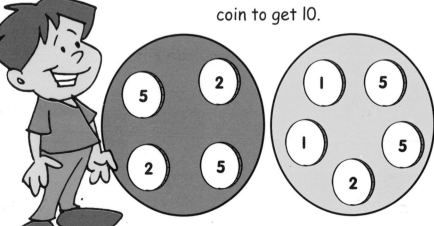

89

Count the total number of hearts and distribute them by drawing the hearts with red colour in each box.

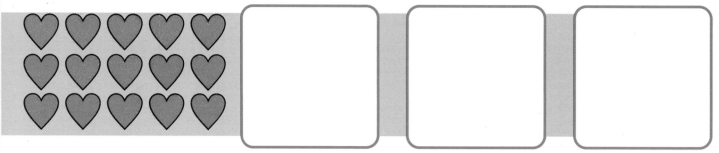

Fill in the missing numbers in the space given below.

	2	3		5		7	8		10
2		6	8	10			16		20

Draw lines to match the correct answers.

Look at the given time and add 2 minutes to each box to find out the answers.

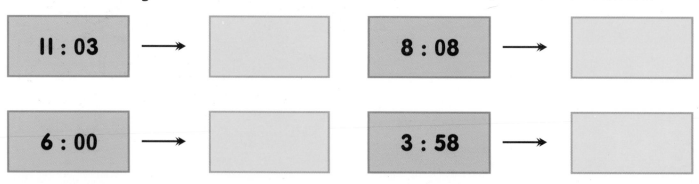

11 : 03 ⟶

8 : 08 ⟶

6 : 00 ⟶

3 : 58 ⟶

Using the code given below colour the boxes.

20 + 9	1 + 8	14 + 5	15 + 10	5 + 2
17 + 2	3 + 4	3 + 6	15 + 8	10 + 6
15 + 15	28 + 6	8 + 1	6 + 4	14 + 3
16 + 3	13 + 9	11 + 6	12 + 7	13 + 5
14 + 8	2 + 8	20 + 10	27 + 4	16 + 9
21 + 6	20 + 3	5 + 4	7 + 3	26 + 3
32 + 5	17 + 6	9 + 2	18 + 2	28 + 4

30 = Red   29 = Yellow   37 = Green   25 = Blue

Use a mirror to solve the sums.

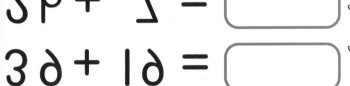

$5P + \lrcorner =$ ☐

$3\partial + 1\partial =$ ☐

How many Ones and Tens are there?

Tens	Ones

Solve the following sums.

16 + _____ = 24

4 + 17 = _____

Solve the puzzle.

	+	2	=	
+		+		+
32	+		=	40
=		=		=
	+	10	=	58

91

Look at the picture and count the objects.

Add the dots on the mushrooms and write the correct answer.

= ◯

= ◯

= ◯

= ◯

Solve the multiplication sum.

X = ☐

Solve the sum.

15 + 15 + 15 + 15 + 15 + 15 = ◯

Fill in the missing numbers.

21

35

7

30

50

10

Solve the puzzle.

5	**+**	**10**	**=**	
+		**+**		**-**
	-	**5**	**=**	
=		**=**		**=**
	-	**15**	**=**	**5**

Count the objects in each set and encircle the correct answer.

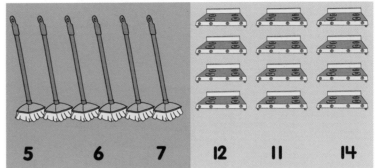

5   6   7   12   11   14

Complete the sums and write the correct answers.

45 - 17 = _____

74 - 65 = _____

66 - 35 = _____

Use the number code to complete the sums.

8   11   15   12   9

Count the big and small stars.

Big Star [ ]   Small Star [ ]

Complete the sequence.

4,   8,   _____,   _____,   _____

8,   _____,   _____,   _____,   40,   _____

Colour the butterflies according to the number given in the centre.

3

Count the objects and match each box with its correct number.

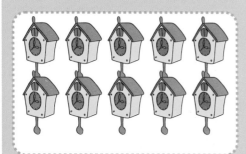

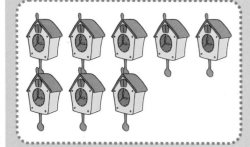

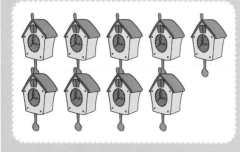

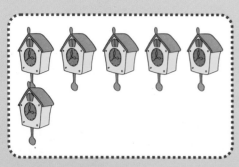

6

9

10

8

Match the sums with their correct answers.

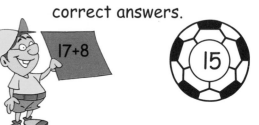 17+8

 15

 32+8

 10

8+2

35

25+10

 40

 12+3

 25

Count and write in the space given below.

Ducks	Rabbits	Birds

Solve the multiplication sums.

___ x ___	___ x ___	___ x ___
___ x ___	___ x ___	___ x ___
___ x ___	___ x ___	___ x ___
___ x ___	___ x ___	___ x ___
36	**45**	**50**

Look at the 3 mosquitoes.
If one of them flies away,
how many will be left there?

_____

Solve the division sums and match each box to the correct group given below.

12 ÷ 4 = ☐   15 ÷ 3 = ☐

14 ÷ 7 = ☐   16 ÷ 4 = ☐

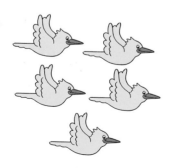   

Solve the sums and use the code to colour the shark.

40 = ● (dark)
50 = ○ (light)

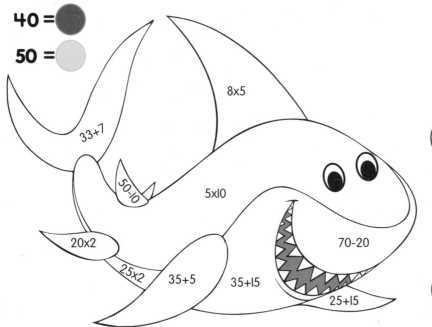

8x5
33+7
50-10
5x10
20x2
25x2
35+5
35+15
70-20
25+15

Help the lion to recognize the bigger number and put the sign ">" or "<" in the blank space.

88 ___ 75

45 ___ 65

Solve the addition sums.

$$\begin{array}{r} 50 \\ +34 \\ \hline \end{array} \qquad \begin{array}{r} 40 \\ +22 \\ \hline \end{array} \qquad \begin{array}{r} 25 \\ +34 \\ \hline \end{array} \qquad \begin{array}{r} 88 \\ +27 \\ \hline \end{array}$$

Solve the number puzzle.

4	+		=	
-				-
1	+		=	2
=		=		=
	+	2	=	5

Solve the sums to get the answer 50.

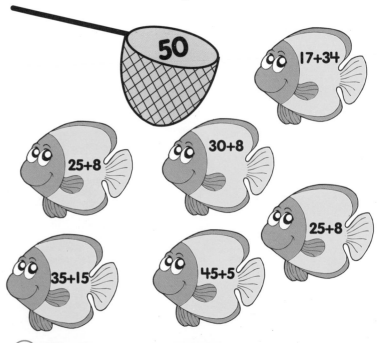

50

17+34

25+8

30+8

25+8

35+15

45+5